Garry Fleming's
Wild Animals
A B C

AN ALPHABET BOOK

 **is for Anemone** *fish*

Anemone fish frolic in the sea, Never swimming far from an anemone!

B is for Bear

I am a
brown
bear,
I am
quite
rare,
There would
be more
of me
If people
showed
more
care!

b

C

is for Crocodile

The crocodile smiles, but just beneath, Lies sharp and pointy crocodile teeth!

C

D is for Dolphin

**Through breaking waves, dolphins leap,
Diving down to oceans deep!**

d

E is for Eagle

An eagle wades along the shore, Watching, waiting, for fish galore!

F is for Frog

See a frog,
Watch it hop,
Into the pond
. . .
Ker-Plop!

G

is for Gorilla

In mountainous jungle thick with lumber,
Gorillas love to sit, and wonder . . .

g

H is for Horse

h

Pounding hooves must be, of course,
The **thundering** sound of a galloping horse!

I

is for Iguanas

i

Iguanas and jaguars have not much in common. Two iguanas smirk slyly, while the jaguar is solemn!

J

is for Jaguar

j

K is for Komodo *dragon*

The komodo is a **hideous** lizard,
With **bowed legs** and an ample gizzard!

L

is for Lion

Lurking amidst dappled light,
Hungry lions wait for night . . .

1

M m

M is for Macaw

N n

N is for Night *monkey*

The scarlet macaw will fill you with **awe,**
But shier than he is the night monkey.

O is for Orangutan

Hanging from a lofty tree, Is where orang-utans love to be!

P

P is for Puma

I have a little hunch . . .
These two pumas are watching lunch!

Q

Q is for Quetzel

In forests lush, and thick, and green, Mysterious quetzels are seldom seen.

q

R is for Rhinoceros

To eat just grass seems **so** preposterous,
When you are as **big** as a huge rhinoceros!

U is for Ulysses *butterfly*

With wings as blue as the bluest sky,
Flies the beautiful Ulysses butterfly!

V is for Vulture

With eyesight so intense and keen,
Vultures always look so mean!

W is for Wolf

Wolves may rest, but will howl with delight, Whenever the moon looms large and bright!

X is for X-ray fish

To have many a friend is its dearest wish,
Such a social creature is the X-ray fish!

X

Y
Y is for Yellow *robin*

y

**Extremely elusive and terribly shy,
A yellow robin might soon flitter by.**

Z is for Zebra

A zebra looks a bit like a horse, Except for his wonderful **stripes**, of course!

Z

This edition published by Scholastic Inc.,
557 Broadway, New York, NY 10012,
by arrangement with Brolly Books.
Scholastic and associated logos are trademarks and/or registered
trademarks of Scholastic Inc.

This edition first published 2009

1 2 3 4 5 6 7 8 9 10

ISBN 978-1-877-03535-7